See Soon, June

by Frannie Rice
illustrated by Louise Ellis

Harcourt
SCHOOL PUBLISHERS

ISBN 10: 0-15-351518-X
ISBN 13: 978-0-15-351518-7

Ordering Options
ISBN 10: 0-15-351214-8 (Grade 4 Advanced Collection)
ISBN 13: 978-0-15-351214-8 (Grade 4 Advanced Collection)
ISBN 10: 0-15-358108-5 (package of 5)
ISBN 13: 978-0-15-358108-3 (package of 5)

3 4 5 6 7 8 9 10 985 12 11 10 09 08

Dear Tim,

Here I am at Camp Green Mountain
on my bunk in my cabin
high above the floor below!
I had to write and say hello.

Everyone else will be here soon.
I'll say to them, "Hi, I'm June!"
I bet I'll make lots of new friends
before the day comes to an end.

Oh, I know I won't have any fear!
I absolutely love it here!

I'll write again soon!

Your friend,

June

Dear June,

You're so lucky to go to camp
where there's a lake and lots of sun.
It's raining here, the house is damp,
and I'm not having any fun.

Grandma and Grandpa's place is nice.
Mom says I will learn to love it here.
It's good to get out of the city once or twice.
She says, "Look, Tim, the sky is so clear!"

Mom says, "I know
you will have lots to do and see,
and then when it's time to go,
you won't want to leave."

I doubt it.

Your friend,

Tim

Dear Tim,

Thanks for your letter—everything is great.
The girls in my cabin are first rate.
They stay up talking in the dark until late.

They were all here last year,
so they all know each other well.
I'm trying to catch up and learn
because then camp will be swell.

You'd love it, too, if you were here.
We'd win races then give a cheer.
Please write soon.

Your friend,

June

Dear June,

It is very quiet here,
like the sound was turned off,
and everything is asleep.

It's not like home,
the city sizzling with sound,
lots of people strolling,
buses clustering all around.
Guess who came to visit today,
my cousin Joe and my cousin Ray.
We swam in a lake,
but I missed the big blue pool,
with the black stripes
and the slide that is, oh, so cool.

I hope things get better soon.
I hope things are fine for you, too, June.

Your friend,

Tim

Dear Tim,

I tried to ride a horse.
I was scared.
"Step on up, June!"
said the teacher.
I took a deep breath
and stepped in her hand.
She pushed me up,
and I was on the horse!

I was a million feet tall
when he started to move,
and I held on tight!

Sara and Lola were learning, too.
We all laughed later
when we admitted we were scared.

Things are better for me here.
I hope they're better for you soon.

Your friend,

June

Dear June,

I learned how to fish. Oh! How I wish
you could have seen how I had to lean
back in the boat,
bouncing afloat
as the fish tugged the line
for such a long time.
Then, at long, long last,
I pulled the fish out fast.
It was fierce but small.
I watched it fall
from my hands
and saw it land
back in the lake.
I couldn't take
it from its place,
but, oh, how I enjoyed the chase!

Things are better, June.
I'll send pictures soon.

Your friend,

Tim

Dear Tim,

We tell stories every night,
trying to give each other a fright.
I told my particular scary tale—
you know it never fails!
Then it's time to surrender to sleep,
and soon you won't hear a peep
as our cheers and laugh riot
turn to deep forest quiet
with just crickets' songs
the whole night long.

I love it here!
Write soon.

Your friend,

June

9

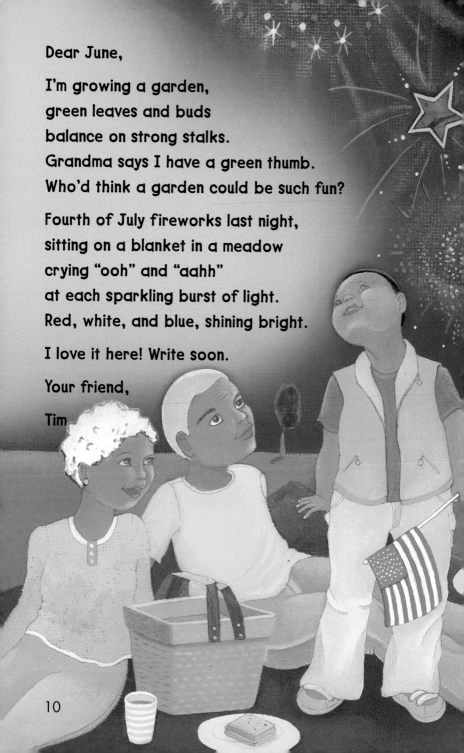

Dear June,

I'm growing a garden,
green leaves and buds
balance on strong stalks.
Grandma says I have a green thumb.
Who'd think a garden could be such fun?

Fourth of July fireworks last night,
sitting on a blanket in a meadow
crying "ooh" and "aahh"
at each sparkling burst of light.
Red, white, and blue, shining bright.

I love it here! Write soon.

Your friend,

Tim

10

Dear Tim,

Field Day at camp, blue sky
no clouds a haze of heat.
All of us like popsicles
melting away into puddles,
but no matter the heat,
we wanted to win,
The girls of Cabin 9.

We ran the first race.
Dashing across
the bumpy grass,

My heart was bursting—
Where was the line?
Then I crossed it,
The champ!
The fastest girl
from Cabin 9.

Now it's time
to leave, at last,
with names, addresses,
photos, numbers,
that all remind me
of friends and days.
I'm sad to leave,
but I miss the city.
I'll be glad to be back
in my home.

See you soon!
Your friend,
June

Dear June,

Remember when
my plants were seed,
then little bits of green,
poking out of the dirt?

Finally, at last,
zucchini, beans,
and best of all, peppers,
never my favorite,
but now they are
because they're mine,
and I grew them
and took care of them.

Thank you,
to Grandma and Grandpa,
for this place,
with its chirping crickets
and buzzing bees,
and the lake
with the fish
that I couldn't quite catch.

I never thought I'd like a place
where it was quiet, where there was
nothing but me and the grass
and the sky and the clouds.
Lying there, looking up,
watching them drift,
and just thinking
and imagining
and wondering.
Who ever thought
you could pass a day
like that?
I'll remember that.

Now I want to come home.
I'll be glad to be back
to talk to you
about our summer.

See you soon, June!

Your friend,

Tim

Think Critically

1. How were June's and Tim's summers different? How were they the same?

2. How did the author organize this poem?

3. How did Tim feel when he arrived at his grandparents' house?

4. What's the first thing that happens that makes June feel better at camp?

5. Would you rather have June's summer or Tim's summer?

⭐ Language Arts

Write a Story Poem Think of something you did or would like to do one summer. Write a story about it in the form of a poem.

 School-Home Connection Choose a section of this poem. Read it aloud with a family member, taking turns with the lines or verses.